Dreamland
BOOK of VERSE

Compiled and designed by Desmond Marwood

Brown Watson
ENGLAND

CONTENTS

ISBN: 0-7097-1374-6

This edition first published 2000 by
Brown Watson, The Old Mill,
76 Fleckney Road, Kibworth Beauchamp,
Leicestershire LE8 0HG

©2000 Brown Watson, England
Printed in the E.C.

The Fairy Folk

Come, cuddle close in Daddy's coat
　　Beside the fire so bright,
And hear about the fairy folk
　　That wander in the night.
For when the stars are shining clear
　　And all the world is still
They float across the silver moon
　　From hill to cloudy hill.

Their caps of red, their cloaks of green,
　　Are hung with silver bells,
And when they're shaken in the wind
　　Their merry ringing swells.
And, riding on the crimson moth
　　With black spots on their wings,
They guide them down the purple sky
　　With golden bridle rings.

They love to visit girls and boys
　　To see how sweet they sleep,
To stand beside their cosy cots
　　And at their faces peep.
For in the whole of fairyland
　　They have no finer sight
Than little children sleeping sound
　　With faces rosy bright.

On tip-toe crowding round their heads
　　When bright the moonlight beams,
They whisper little tender words
　　That fill their minds with dreams;
And when they see a sunny smile,
　　With lightest finger tips,
They lay a hundred kisses sweet
　　Upon the ruddy lips.

And then the little spotted moths
　　Spread out their crimson wings,
And bear away the fairy crowd
　　With shaking bridle rings.
Come, bairnies, hide in Daddy's coat
　　Beside the fire so bright –
Perhaps the little folk
　　Will visit you tonight.

ROBERT BIRD

3

The Fly-Away Horse

Oh, a wonderful horse is the Fly-Away Horse,
    Perhaps you have seen him before;
Perhaps while you slept his shadow has swept
    Through the moonlight that floats on the floor.
For it's only at night, when the stars twinkle bright,
    That the Fly-Away Horse, with a neigh
And a pull at his rein and a toss of his mane,
    Is up on his heels and away!
The moon in the sky,
    As he gallopeth by,
Cries: "Oh, what a marvellous sight!"
    And the stars in dismay
Hide their faces away
    In the lap of old Grandmother Night.

It is yonder, out yonder, the Fly-Away Horse
    Speedeth ever and ever away –
Over meadows and lanes, over mountains and plains,
    Over streamlets that sing at their play;
And over the sea like a ghost sweepeth he,
    While the ships they go sailing below,
And he speedeth so fast that the men at the mast
    Adjudge him some portent of woe,
"What ho there!" they cry
    As he flourishes by
With a whisk of his beautiful tail;
    And the fish in the sea
Are as scared as can be,
    From the nautilus up to the whale!

And the Fly-Away Horse seeks those faraway lands,
  You little folk dream of at night –
Where candy-trees grow, and honey brooks flow,
  And cornfields with popcorn are white;
And the beasts in the wood are ever so good
  To children who visit them there –
What glory astride of a lion to ride,
  Or to wrestle around with a bear!
The monkeys, they say:
  "Come on, let us play,"
And they frisk in the coconut trees:
  While the parrots that cling
To the peanut vines sing
  Or converse with comparative ease!

Off! Scamper to bed – you shall ride him tonight,
  For, as soon as you've fallen asleep,
With a jubilant neigh he will bear you away
  Over forest and hillside and deep!
But tell us, my dear, all you see and you hear
  In those beautiful lands over there,
Where the Fly-Away Horse wings his faraway course
  With the wee one consigned to his care.
Then Grandma will cry
  In amazement: "Oh, my!"
And she'll think it could never be so;
  And only we two
Shall know it is true –
  You and I, little precious, shall know!

5   EUGENE FIELD

The Land of Nod

From breakfast on all through the day
    At home among my friends I stay;
But every night I go abroad
    Afar into the land of Nod.

All by myself I have to go,
    With none to tell me what to do –
All alone beside the streams
    And up the mountainsides of dreams.

The strangest things are there for me,
    Both things to eat and things to see,
And many frightening sights abroad
    Till morning in the land of Nod.

Try as I like to find the way,
    I never can get back by day,
Nor can remember plain and clear
    The curious music that I hear.

ROBERT LOUIS STEVENSON

Hush Little Baby

Hush little baby, don't say a word,
    Papa's going to buy you a mocking-bird.
If that mocking-bird won't sing,
    Papa's going to buy you a diamond ring.
If that diamond ring turns brass,
    Papa's going to buy you a looking glass.
If that looking glass gets broke,
    Papa's going to buy you a billy goat.
If that billy goat won't pull,
    Papa's going to buy you a cart and bull.
If that cart and bull fall down,
    You'll still be the sweetest little baby in town.

ANONYMOUS

The Rock-a-by Lady

The Rock-a-by Lady from Hush-a-by Street
 Comes stealing; comes creeping;
The poppies they hang from her head to her feet,
 And each hath a dream that is tiny and fleet –
She bringeth her poppies to you, my sweet,
 When she findeth you sleeping.

There is one little dream of a beautiful drum –
 "Rub-a-dub!" it goeth;
There is one little dream of a big sugar plum,
 And lo! thick and fast the other dreams come
Of popguns that bang, and tin tops that hum,
 And the trumpet that bloweth.

And dollies peep out of those wee little dreams
 With laughter and singing;
And boats go a-floating on silvery streams,
 And the stars peek-a-boo with their own misty gleams,
And up, up and up, where Mother Moon beams,
 The fairies go winging!

Would you dream all these dreams that are tiny and fleet?
 They'll come to you sleeping;
So shut the two eyes that are weary, my sweet,
 For the Rock-a-by Lady from Hush-a-by Street,
With poppies that hang from her head to her feet,
 Comes stealing, comes creeping.

EUGENE FIELD

The Flowers

All the names I know from nurse:
    Gardener's Garters, Shepherd's Purse,
Batchelor's Buttons, Lady's Smock,
    And the Lady Hollyhock.

Fairy places, fairy things,
    Fairy woods where the wild bee wings,
Tiny trees for tiny dames –
    These must all be fairy names!

Tiny woods below whose boughs
    Shady fairies weave a house;
Tiny tree-tops, rose or thyme,
    Where the braver fairies climb!

Fair are grown-up people's trees,
    But the fairest woods are these;
Where if I were not so tall,
    I should live for good and all.

ROBERT LOUIS STEVENSON

Young Night Thought

All night long, and every night,
    When my mamma puts out the light,
I see the people marching by,
    As plain as day, before my eye.

Armies and emperors and kings,
    All carrying different kinds of things,
And marching in so grand a way,
    You never saw the like by day.

So fine a show was never seen
    At the great circus on the green;
For every kind of beast and man
    Is marching in that caravan.

At first they move a little slow,
    But still the faster on they go,
And still beside them close I keep
    Until we reach the town of Sleep.

ROBERT LOUIS STEVENSON

Where Go The Boats?

Dark brown is the river,
    Golden is the sand,
It flows along for ever,
    With trees on either hand.

Green leaves a-floating,
    Castles of the foam,
Boats of mine a-boating –
    Where will all come home?

On goes the river
    And out past the mill,
Away down the valley,
    Away down the hill.

Away down the river,
    A hundred miles or more,
Other little children
    Shall bring my boats ashore.

ROBERT LOUIS STEVENSON

Travel

I should like to rise and go
    Where the golden apples grow;
Where, below another sky
    Parrot islands anchored lie,
And, watched by cockatoos and goats,
    Lonely Crusoes building boats;
Where, in sunshine reaching out,
    Eastern cities, miles about,
Are with mosque and minaret
    Among sandy gardens set,
And the rich goods from near and far
    Hang for sale in the bazaar;
Where the Great Wall round China goes,
    And on one side the desert blows,
And with bell and voice and drum,
    Cities on the other hum;

Where are forests, hot as fire,
    Wide as England, tall as a spire,
Full of apes and coco-nuts
    And negro hunters' huts;
Where the knotty crocodile
    Lies and blinks in the Nile,
And the red flamingo flies
    Hunting fish before his eyes;
Where in jungles, near and far,
    Man-devouring tigers are,
Lying close and giving ear,
    Lest the hunt be drawing near,
Or a comer-by be seen
    Swinging in a palanquin;
Where among the desert sands
    Some deserted city stands,

All its children, sweep and prince,
  Grown to manhood ages since,
Not a foot in street or house,
  Not a stir of child or mouse,
And when kindly falls the night,
  In all the town no spark of light.
There I'll come when I'm a man
  With a camel caravan;
Light a fire in the gloom
  Of some dusty dining-room;
See the pictures on the walls,
  Heroes, fights and festivals;
And in a corner find the toys
  Of the old Egyptian boys.

ROBERT LOUIS STEVENSON

The Owl and the Pussycat

The Owl and the Pussycat went to sea
   In a beautiful pea-green boat,
They took some honey and plenty of money,
   Wrapped in a five-pound note.
The Owl looked up to the stars above,
   And sang to a small guitar,
"O lovely Pussy! O Pussy, my love,
   What a beautiful Pussy you are,
      You are,
      You are!
What a beautiful Pussy you are!"

Pussy said to the Owl, "You elegant fowl!
   How charmingly sweet you sing!
Oh, let us be married! Too long have we tarried:
   But what shall we do for a ring?"
They sailed away, for a year and a day,
   To the land where the Bong-tree grows,
And there in a wood a Piggy-wig stood,
   With a ring at the end of his nose,
      His nose,
      His nose,
   With a ring at the end of his nose.

"Dear Pig, are you willing to sell for one shilling
   Your ring?" Said the Piggy, "I will."
So they took it away, and were married next day
   By the Turkey who lives on the hill.
They dined on mince and slices of quince,
   Which they ate with a runcible spoon;
And hand in hand, on the edge of the sand,
   They danced by the light of the moon,
      The moon,
      The moon,
   They danced by the light of the moon.

EDWARD LEAR

Monday's Child

Monday's child is fair of face,
 Tuesday's child is full of grace,
Wednesday's child is full of woe,
 Thursday's child has far to go,
Friday's child is loving and giving,
 Saturday's child works hard for its living,
And a child that's born on the Sabbath day
 Is fair and wise and good at play.

ANONYMOUS

A Good Play

We built a ship upon the stairs
 All made of the back-bedroom chairs,
And filled it full of sofa pillows
 To go a-sailing on the billows.

We took a saw and several nails,
 And water in the nursery pails;
And Tom said, "Let us also take
 An apple and a slice of cake,"
Which was enough for Tom and me
 To go a-sailing on, till tea.

We sailed along for days and days,
 And had the very best of plays;
But Tom fell out and hurt his knee,
 So there was no one left but me.

ROBERT LOUIS STEVENSON

City Mouse and Garden Mouse

The city mouse lives in a house,
   The garden mouse lives in a bower;
He's friendly with the frogs and toads,
   And sees pretty plants in flower.

The city mouse eats bread and cheese,
   The garden mouse eats what he can;
We will not grudge him seeds and stocks,
   Poor little timid, furry man.

CHRISTINA ROSSETTI

To a Butterfly

I've watched you now a full half-hour,
   Self-poised upon that yellow flower;
And, little butterfly, indeed
   I know not if you sleep or feed.
How motionless! Not frozen seas
   More motionless! And then
What joy awaits you when the breeze
   Hath found you out among the trees,
And calls you forth again!

This plot of orchard ground is ours:
   My trees they are, my sister's flowers.
Here rest your wings when they are weary,
   Here lodge as in a sanctuary!
Come often to us, fear no wrong;
   Sit near us on the bough!
We'll talk of sunshine and of song,
   And summer days when we were young;
Sweet childish days that were as long
   As twenty days are now.

WILLIAM WORDSWORTH

Laughing Song

When the green woods laugh with the voice of joy
   And the dimpling stream turns laughing by,
When the air does laugh with merry wit,
   And the green hill laughs with the noise of it;

When the meadows laugh with lively green,
   And the grasshopper laughs in the merry scene;
When Mary, and Susan, and Emily
   With their sweet sounding mouths sing, "Ha, ha, he!"

When the painted birds laugh in the shade,
   Where our table with cherries and nuts is spread:
Come live, and be merry, and join with me,
   To sing the sweet chorus of "Ha, ha, he!"

WILLIAM BLAKE

The Fairies

Up the airy mountain,
    Down the rushy glen,
We daren't go a-hunting
    For fear of little men;
Wee folk, good folk,
    Trooping all together;
Green jacket, red cap,
    And white owl's feather!

Down along the rocky shore,
    Some make their home,
They live on crispy pancakes
    Of yellow tide-foam;
Some in the reeds
    Of the black mountain lake,
With frogs for their watchdogs,
    All night awake.

High on the hill-top
    The old King sits;
He is now so old and grey
    He's nigh lost his wits.
With a bridge of white mist
    Columbkill he crosses,
On his stately journeys
    From Slieveleague to Rosses.

Or going up with music
    On cold, starry nights,
To sup with the Queen
    Of the gay Northern Lights.
They stole little Bridget
    For seven years long;
When she came down again
    Her friends were all gone.

They took her lightly back,
    Between the night and morrow,
They thought that she was fast asleep,
    But she was dead with sorrow.
They have kept her ever since
    Deep within the lake,
On a bed of flag-leaves,
    Watching till she wake.

By the craggy hillside,
    Through the mosses bare,
They have planted thorn trees
    For pleasure here and there.
Is any man so daring
    As dig them up in spite,
He shall find their sharpest thorns
    In his bed at night.

Up the airy mountain,
    Down the rushy glen,
We daren't go a-hunting
    For fear of little men;
Wee folk, good folk,
    Trooping all together;
Green jacket, red cap,
    And white owl's feather!

WILLIAM ALLINGHAM

Mister Nobody

I know a funny little man,
    As quiet as a mouse,
Who does the mischief that is done
    In everybody's house!
There's no one ever sees his face,
    And yet we all agree
That every plate we break was cracked
    By Mister Nobody.

'Tis he who always tears our books,
    Who leaves the door ajar,
He pulls the buttons from our shirts,
    And scatters pins afar;
That squeaking door will always squeak
    For, prithee don't you see,
We leave the oiling to be done
    By Mister Nobody.

He puts damp wood upon the fire,
    That kettles cannot boil;
His are the feet that bring in mud,
    And all the carpets soil.
The papers always are mislaid,
    Who had them last but he?
There's no one tosses them about
    But Mister Nobody.

The finger marks upon the door
    By none of us are made;
We never leave the blinds unclosed
    To let the curtains fade;
The ink we never spill; the boots
    That lying round you see
Are not our boots – they all belong
    To Mister Nobody.

ANONYMOUS

Autumn Fires

In the other gardens
  And all up the vale,
From the autumn bonfires
  See the smoke trail!

Pleasant summer over
  And all the summer flowers,
The red fire blazes,
  The grey smoke towers.

Sing a song of seasons!
  Something bright in all!
Flowers in the summer,
  Fires in the fall!

ROBERT LOUIS STEVENSON

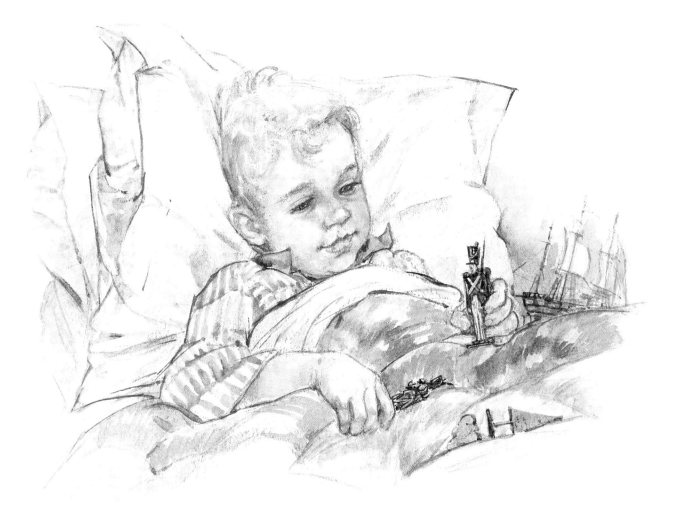

The Land of Counterpane

When I was sick and lay a-bed,
　I had two pillows at my head,
And all my toys beside me lay
　To keep me happy all the day.

And sometimes for an hour or so
　I watched my leaden soldiers go,
With different uniforms and drills,
　Among the bed-clothes, through the hills.

And sometimes sent my ships in fleets
　All up and down among the sheets;
Or brought my trees and houses out,
　And planted cities all about.

I was the giant great and still
　That sits upon the pillow-hill,
And sees before him, dale and plain,
　The pleasant land of counterpane.

ROBERT LOUIS STEVENSON

The Robin

When up aloft
   I fly and fly,
I see in pools
   The shining sky,
And a happy bird
   Am I, am I!

When I descend
   Toward the brink
I stand and look
   And stop and drink
And bathe my wings,
   And chink and prink.

When winter frost
   Makes earth as steel,
I search and search
   But find no meal,
And most unhappy
   Then I feel.

But when it lasts,
   And snows still fall,
I get to feel
   No grief at all,
For I turn to a cold, stiff
   Feather ball!

THOMAS HARDY

The Kitten and the Leaves

See the kitten on the wall,
    Sporting with the leaves that fall,
Withered leaves – one, two, and three –
    From the lofty elder tree!
Through the calm and frosty air
    Of this morning bright and fair,
Eddying round and round, they sink
    Softly, slowly: one might think,
From the motions that are made,
    Every little leaf conveyed
Sylph or fairy hither tending,
    To this lower world descending,
Each invisible and mute
    In his wavering parachute.
But the kitten, how she starts,
    Crouches, stretches, paws and darts,
First at one, and then its fellow,
    Just as light and just as yellow;
There are many now – now one –
    Now they stop and there are none:
What intenseness of desire
    In her upward eye of fire!
With a tiger-leap halfway
    Now she meets the coming prey,
Let it go as fast, and then
    Has it in her power again:
How she works with three or four,
    Like an Indian conjuror:
Quick as he in feats of art,
    Far beyond his joy of heart.
Were her antics played in the eye
    Of a thousand standers-by
Clapping hands with shouts and stare,
    What would little Tabby care
For the plaudits of the crowd?
    Over happy to be proud,
Over wealthy in the treasure
    Of her own exceeding pleasure!

WILLIAM WORDSWORTH

22

Dobbin's Friend

Dobbin has a little friend,
    Spotted white and sable;
Every day she goes to him
    In his lonely stable.

Not a mite of dread has she,
    Not a thought of danger;
Lightly runs between his hoofs,
    Jumps upon his manger;

Lays her soft, warm cheek to his,
    Purrs her meek: "Good morning!"
Gives the flies that hover near
    Such a look of warning!

"Dobbin dear," she sometimes says,
    "Feel my winter mittens!
Nice and warm, you see, and made
    Purposely for kittens.

"Dobbin dear, such times at home!
    Mother has caught a rat!
Brought it home to show us.
    What do you think of that?

"Dobbin," she whispers, purring still,
    "You often get so weary!
Why don't you balk or run away,
    And get your freedom, dearie?"

Then Dobbin gives his head a toss,
    And says: "For shame, Miss Kitty!
If I could do such a mean thing
    'Twould be a monstrous pity!

"No, no, my master's good and kind!
    I'll never vex him – never!"
And Kitty, pleased, still rubs his cheek,
    And likes him more than ever.

MARY MAPES DODGE

The Moon

The moon has a face like the clock in the hall;
　　She shines on thieves on the garden wall,
On streets and fields and harbour quays,
　　And birdies asleep in the forks of the trees.

The squalling cat and the squeaking mouse,
　　The howling dog by the door of the house,
The bat that lies in bed at noon,
　　All love to be out by the light of the moon.

But all of the things that belong to the day
　　Cuddle to sleep to be out of her way;
And flowers and children close their eyes
　　Till up in the morning the sun shall rise.

ROBERT LOUIS STEVENSON

Is the Moon Tired?

Is the moon tired? She looks so pale
　　Within her misty veil;
She scales the sky from east to west,
　　And takes no rest.

Before the coming of the night
　　The moon shows papery white;
Before the dawning of the day
　　She fades away.

CHRISTINA ROSSETTI

Foreign Lands

Up into the cherry tree
    Who should climb but little me?
I held the trunk with both my hands
    And looked abroad on foreign lands.

I saw the next-door garden lie,
    Adorned with flowers before my eye,
And many pleasant places more
    That I had never seen before.

I saw the dimpling river pass
    And be the sky's blue looking-glass;
The dusty roads go up and down
    With people tramping into town.

If I could find a higher tree
    Farther and farther I should see
To where the grown-up river slips
    Into the sea among the ships.

To where the roads on either hand
    Lead onward into fairy land,
Where all the children dine at five,
    And all the playthings come alive.

ROBERT LOUIS STEVENSON

The Tiger

Tiger! Tiger! burning bright
   In the forests of the night,
What immortal hand or eye
   Could frame thy fearful symmetry?

In what distant deeps or skies
   Burnt the fire of thine eyes?
On what wings dare he aspire?
   What the hand dare seize the fire?

And what shoulder and what art
   Could twist the sinews of thy heart?
And, when thy heart began to beat,
   What dread hand forged thy dread feet?

What the hammer, what the chain,
   In what furnace was thy brain?
What the anvil? What dread grasp
   Dare its deadly terrors clasp?

When the stars threw down their spears,
   And watered heaven with their tears,
Did He smile His work to see?
   Did He who made the lamb make thee?

Tiger! Tiger! burning bright
   In the forests of the night,
What immortal hand or eye
   Dare frame thy fearful symmetry?

WILLIAM BLAKE

Eldorado

Gaily bedight,
   A gallant knight,
In sunshine and in shadow,
   Had journeyed long,
Singing a song,
   In search of Eldorado.

But he grew old –
   This knight so bold –
And o'er his heart a shadow
   Fell, as he found
No spot of ground
   That looked like Eldorado.

And, as his strength
   Failed him at length,
He met a pilgrim shadow
   "Shadow," said he,
"Where can it be –
   This land of Eldorado?"

"Over the Mountains
   Of the Moon,
Down the Valley of the Shadow,
   Ride, boldly ride,"
The shade replied,
   "If you seek for Eldorado!"

EDGAR ALLAN POE

The Hag

The Hag is astride,
    This night for to ride,
The Devil and she together:
    Through thick and through thin,
Now out, and then in,
    Though ne'er so foul be the weather.

A Thorn or a Burr
    She takes for a spur:
With a lash of a Bramble she rides now,
    Through Brakes and through Briars,
O'oer Ditches and Mires,
    She follows the Spirit that guides now.

No Beast, for his food,
    Dares now range the wood;
But hushed in his lair he lies lurking;
    While mischiefs by these,
On Land and on Seas,
    At noon of Night are a-working.

The storms will arise,
    And trouble the skies;
This night, and more for the wonder,
    The ghost from the Tomb
Affrighted shall come,
    Called out by the clap of the Thunder.

ROBERT HERRICK

The Owl

When cats run home and light has come,
　　And dew is cold upon the ground,
And the far-off stream is dumb,
　　And the whirring sails go round,
　　And the whirring sails go round;
Alone and warming his five wits,
　　The white owl in the belfry sits.

When merry milkmaids click the latch,
　　And rarely smells the new-mown hay,
And the cock hath sung beneath the thatch
　　Twice or thrice his roundelay,
　　Twice or thrice his roundelay;
Alone and warming his five wits,
　　The white owl in the belfry sits.

ALFRED, LORD TENNYSON

The Perfect Greyhound

If you would have a good tyke,
　　Of which there are few like –
He must be headed like a snake,
　　Necked like a drake,
Backed like a bream,
　　Sided like a bream,
Tailed like a bat,
　　And footed like a cat.

ANONYMOUS

The Swing

How do you like to go up in a swing,
    Up in the air so blue?
Oh, I do think it the pleasantest thing
    Ever a child can do!

Up in the air and over the wall,
    Till I can see so wide,
Rivers and trees and cattle and all
    Over the countryside –

Till I look down on the garden green,
    Down on the roof so brown –
Up in the air I go flying again,
    Up in the air and down!

ROBERT LOUIS STEVENSON

I Wandered Lonely As A Cloud

I wandered lonely as a cloud
   That floats on high o'er vales and hills,
When all at once I saw a crowd,
   A host, of golden daffodils;
Beside the lake, beneath the trees,
   Fluttering and dancing in the breeze.

Continuous as the stars that shine
   And twinkle on the Milky Way,
They stretched in never-ending line
   Along the margin of a bay:
Ten thousand saw I at a glance,
   Tossing their heads in sprightly dance.

The waves beside them danced, but they
   Out-did the sparkling waves in glee:
A poet could not but be gay,
   In such jocund company:
I gazed – and gazed – but little thought
   What wealth the show to me had brought:

For oft, when on my couch I lie,
   In vacant or in pensive mood,
They flash upon that inward eye
   Which is the bliss of solitude;
And then my heart with pleasure fills,
   And dances with the daffodils.

WILLIAM WORDSWORTH

The Shut-Eye Train

Come, my little one, with me!
    There are wondrous sights to see
As the evening shadows fall,
    In your pretty cap and gown.
Don't detain
    The Shut-Eye Train –
"Ting-a-ling!" the bell it goeth,
    "Toot-toot!" the whistle bloweth,
And we hear the warning call:
    "All aboard for Shut-Eye Town!"

Over hill and over plain
    Soon will speed the Shut-Eye train!
Through the blue where bloom the stars,
    And the Mother Moon looks down,
We'll away
    To land of Fay.
Oh, the sights that we shall see there!
    Come, my little one, with me there –
'Tis a goodly train of cars –
    All aboard for Shut-Eye Town.

Swifter than the wild bird's flight,
   Through the realms of fleecy night
We shall speed and speed away!
   Let the night with envy frown –
What care we
   How wroth she be!
To the Balow-land above us,
   To the Balow-folk who love us,
Let us hasten while we may –
   All aboard for Shut-Eye Town!

Shut-Eye Town is passing fair,
   Golden dreams await us there;
We shall dream those dreams, my dear,
   Till the Mother Moon goes down –
See unfold
   Delights untold!
And in those mysterious places
   We shall see beloved faces,
And beloved voices hear
   In the grace of Shut-Eye Town.

Heavy are our eyes my sweet,
   Weary are our little feet –
Nestle closer up to me
   In your pretty cap and gown;
Don't detain
   The Shut-Eye Train!
"Ting-a-ling!" the bell it goeth,
   "Toot-toot!" the whistle bloweth,
Oh, the sights that we shall see!
   All aboard for Shut-Eye Town!

EUGENE FIELD

Bed in Summer

In winter I get up at night
   And dress by yellow candle-light,
In summer, quite the other way,
   I have to go to bed by day.

I have to go to bed and see
   The birds still hopping on the tree,
Or hear the grown-up people's feet
   Still going past me in the street.

And does it not seem hard to you,
   When all the sky is clear and blue,
And I should like so much to play,
   To have to go to bed by day?

ROBERT LOUIS STEVENSON

Topsy-Turvy World

If the butterfly courted the bee,
    And the owl the porcupine;
If churches were built in the sea,
    And three times one was nine;
If the pony rode his master,
    If the buttercups ate the cows,
If the cat had the dire disaster,
    To be worried, sir, by the mouse;
If mamma, sir, sold the baby
    To a gipsy for half-a-crown;
If a gentleman, sir, was a lady,
    The world would be Upside-Down!
If any of all these wonders
    Should ever come about
I should not consider them blunders,
    For I should be Inside-Out!

Baa baa, black wool,
    Have you any sheep?
Yes, sir, a packfull,
    Creep, mouse, creep!
Four-and-twenty little maids
    Hanging out the pie,
Out jumped the honey-pot,
    Guy Fawkes, Guy!
Cross latch, cross latch,
    Sit and spin the fire,
When the pie was opened,
    The bird was on the brier!

WILLIAM BRIGHTY RANDS

The Sugar-Plum Tree

Have you ever heard of the Sugar-Plum Tree?
    'Tis a marvel of great renown!
It blooms on the shores of the Lollipop Sea
    In the garden of Shut-Eye Town;
The fruit that it bears is so wondrously sweet
    (As those who have tasted it say)
That good little children have only to eat
    Of that fruit to be happy next day.

When you've got to the tree, you would have a hard time
    To capture the fruit which I sing;
The tree is so tall that no person could climb
    To the bough where the sugar-plums swing!
But up in that tree sits a chocolate cat,
    And a gingerbread dog prowls below –
And this is the way you contrive to get at
    Those sugar-plums tempting you so.

You say but the word to that gingerbread dog
    And he barks with such terrible zest
That the chocolate cat is at once all agog,
    As her swelling proportions attest.
And the chocolate cat goes cavorting around
    From this leafy limb unto that,
And the sugar-plums tumble, of course, to the ground –
    Hurrah for the chocolate cat!

There are marshmallows, gumdrops, and peppermint canes
    With stripings of scarlet or gold,
And you carry away of the treasure that rains
    As much as your apron can hold!
So come, little child, cuddle closer to me
    In your dainty white nightcap and gown,
And I'll rock you away to that Sugar-Plum Tree
    In the garden of Shut-Eye-Town.

EUGENE FIELD

35

The Pedlar's Caravan

I wish I lived in a caravan,
　With a horse to drive, like a pedlar-man!
Where he comes from nobody knows,
　Or where he goes to, but on he goes!

His caravan has windows two,
　And a chimney of tin, that the smoke comes through;
He has a wife, with a baby brown,
　And they go riding, from town to town.

Chairs to mend and delf to sell!
　He clashes the basins like a bell;
Tea-trays, baskets, ranged in order,
　Plates with the alphabet round the border!

The roads are brown, and the sea is green,
　But his house is just like a bathing machine;
The world is round, and he can ride,
　Rumble and splash, to the other side!

With the pedlar-man I should like to roam,
　And write a book when I came home;
All the people would read my book,
　Just like the Travels of Captain Cook!

WILLIAM BRIGHTY RANDS

Boy's Song

Where the pools are bright and deep,
   Where the grey trout lies asleep,
Up the river and over the lea,
   That's the way for Billy and me.

Where the blackbird sings the latest,
   Where the hawthorn blooms the sweetest,
Where the nestlings chirp and flee,
   That's the way for Billy and me.

Where the mowers mow the cleanest,
   Where the hay lies thick and greenest,
There to track the homeward bee,
   That's the way for Billy and me.

Where the hazel bank is steepest,
   Where the shadow falls the deepest,
Where the clustering nuts fall free,
   That's the way for Billy and me.

Why the boys should drive away
   Little sweet maidens from the play,
Or love to banter and fight so well,
   That's the thing I could never tell.

But this I know, I love to play
   Through the meadow, among the hay;
Up the water and o'er the lea,
   That's the way for Billy and me.

JAMES HOGG

37

Summer Sun

Great is the sun, and wide he goes
    Through empty heaven without repose;
And in the blue and glowing days
    More thick than rain he showers his rays.

Though closer still the blinds we pull
    To keep the shady parlour cool,
Yet he will find a chink or two
    To slip his golden fingers through.

The dusty attic, spider-clad,
    He, through the keyhole, maketh glad;
And through the broken edge of tiles,
    Into the laddered hayloft smiles.

Meantime his golden face around
    He bears to all the garden ground,
And sheds a warm and glittering look
    Among the ivy's inmost nook.

Above the hills, along the blue,
    Round the bright air with footing true,
To please the child, to paint the rose,
    The gardener of the World, he goes.

ROBERT LOUIS STEVENSON

My Shadow

I have a little shadow that goes in and out with me,
    And what can be the use of him is more than I can see.
He is very, very like me from the heels up to the head;
    And I see him jump before me when I jump into my bed.

The funniest thing about him is the way he likes to grow –
    Not at all like proper children, which is always very slow;
For he sometimes shoots up taller, like an india-rubber ball,
    And he sometimes gets so little that there's none of him at all.

He hasn't got a notion of how children ought to play,
    And can only make a fool of me in every sort of way.
He stays so close behind me he's a coward you can see;
    I'd think shame to stick to nursie as that shadow sticks to me!

One morning, very early, before the sun was up,
    I rose and found the shining dew on every buttercup;
But my lazy little shadow, like an arrant sleepy-head,
    Had stayed at home behind me and was fast asleep in bed.

ROBERT LOUIS STEVENSON

39

The Village Blacksmith

Under a spreading chestnut tree
   The village smithy stands;
The smith, a mighty man is he,
   With large and sinewy hands;
And the muscles of his brawny arms
   Are strong as iron bands.

His hair is crisp, and black, and long,
   His face is like the tan;
His brow is wet with honest sweat,
   He earns whate'er he can;
And looks the whole world in the face,
   For he owes not any man.

Week in, week out, from morn till night,
   You can hear his bellows blow;
You can hear him swing his heavy sledge
   With measure beat and slow,
Like a sexton ringing the village bell
   When the evening sun is low.

And children coming home from school
   Look in at the open door;
They love to see the flaming forge
   And hear the bellows roar,
And catch the burning sparks that fly
   Like chaff from a threshing-floor.

He goes on Sunday to the church,
   And sits among his boys;
He hears the parson pray and preach,
   He hears his daughter's voice
Singing in the village choir,
   And makes his heart rejoice.

It sounds to him like her mother's voice
   Singing in Paradise!
He needs must think of her once more
   How in the grave she lies,
And with his hard, rough hand he wipes
   A tear out of his eyes.

Toiling, rejoicing, sorrowing,
   Onward through life he goes;
Each morning sees some task begun,
   Each evening sees it close.
Something attempted, something done,
   Has earned a night's repose.

Thanks, thanks to thee, my worthy friend
   For the lesson though hast taught!
Thus at the flaming forge of Life
   Our fortunes must be wrought;
Thus on its sounding anvil shaped
   Each burning deed and thought!

HENRY WADSWORTH LONGFELLOW

Winter

When icicles hang by the wall,
  And Dick the shepherd blows his nail,
And Tom bears logs into the hall,
  And milk comes frozen home in pail;

When blood is nipped, and ways be foul,
  Then nightly sings the staring owl,
Tu-whit, tu-whoo! A merry note,
  While greasy Joan doth keel the pot.

When all aloud the wind doth blow,
  And coughing drowns the parson's saw
And birds sit brooding in the snow,
  And Marian's nose looks red and raw,

When roasted crabs hiss in the bowl,
  Then nightly sings the staring owl.
Tu-whit, tu-whoo! A merry note,
  While greasy Joan doth keel the pot.

WILLIAM SHAKESPEARE

Fall, Leaves, Fall

Fall, leaves, fall: die, flowers, away;
  Lengthen night and shorten day,
Every leaf speaks bliss to me
  Fluttering from the autumn tree.

I shall smile when wreaths of snow
  Blossom where the rose should grow;
I shall sing when night's decay
  Ushers in a drearier day.

EMILY BRONTË

Another Plum-Cake

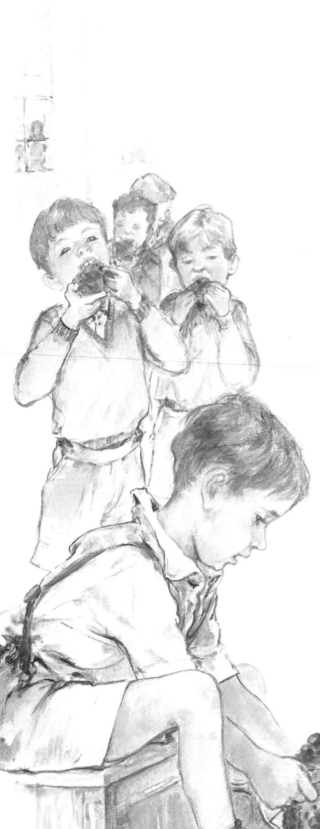

"Oh! I've got a plum-cake, and a feast let us make;
     Come, schoolfellows, come at my call;
I assure you 'tis nice, and we'll each have a slice,
     Here's more than enough for us all."

Thus said little Jack, as he gave it a smack,
     And sharpen'd his knife to begin;
Nor was there one found, upon the play-ground,
     So cross that he would not come in.

With masterly strength, he cut through it at length,
     And gave to each playmate a share:
Charles, William, and James, and many more names,
     Partook his benevolent care.

And when it was done, and they'd finished their fun,
     To marbles or hoop they went back;
And each little boy felt it always a joy,
     To do a good turn for good Jack.

In his task and his book, his best pleasures he took,
     And as he thus wisely began,
Since he's been a man grown he has constantly shown
     That a good boy will make a good man.

ANN and JANE TAYLOR

A Tragic Story

There lived a sage in days of yore,
   And he a handsome pigtail wore;
But wondered much, and sorrowed more,
   Because it hung behind him.

He mused upon this serious case,
   And swore he'd change the pigtail's place
And have it hanging at his face,
   Not dangling there behind him.

Says he: "The mystery I've found –
   I'll turn me round" – he turned around,
But still it hung behind him.

Then round and round, and out and in,
   All day the puzzled sage did spin;
In vain – it mattered not a pin –
   The pigtail hung behind him.

And right and left, and round about,
   And up and down, and in and out,
He turned – but still the pigtail stout
   Hung steadily behind him.

And though his efforts never slack,
   And though he twist and twirl and tack,
Alas, still faithful to his back,
   The pigtail hangs behind him!

OF UNKNOWN GERMAN ORIGIN
(Believed to have been translated by William Thackeray)

What Would You Do?

Oh, what would you do if you had a cow
    Who never said: "Moo!" but preferred: "Bow-wow!";
Who played the guitar and lived in a sty,
    And put on goloshes to keep her feet dry!

ANONYMOUS

Time to Rise

A birdie with a yellow bill
    Hopped upon the window sill,
Cocked his shining eye and said:
    "Ain't you shamed, you sleepy head?"

ROBERT LOUIS STEVENSON

If You Should Meet a Crocodile

If you should meet a crocodile,
    Don't take a stick and poke him;
Ignore the welcome in his smile,
    Be careful not to stroke him.

For as he sleeps upon the Nile,
    He thinner gets and thinner;
And whene'er you meet a crocodile
    He's ready for his dinner.

The Eagle

He clasps the crag with crooked hands;
    Close to the sun in lonely lands,
Ringed with the azure world he stands.

The wrinkled sea beneath him crawls;
    He watches from his mountain walls,
And like a thunderbolt he falls.

ALFRED, LORD TENNYSON

ANONYMOUS

Jemima

There was a little girl, she wore a little hood,
    And a curl down the middle of her forehead,
When she was good, she was very, very good,
    But when she was bad, she was horrid.

One day she went upstairs, while her parents, unawares,
    In the kitchen down below were occupied with meals,
And she stood upon her head, on her little truckle-bed,
    And she then began hurraying with her heels.

Her mother heard the noise, and thought it was the boys,
    A-playing at a combat in the attic,
But when she climbed the stair and saw Jemima there,
    She rebuked her naughty daughter most emphatic!

ANONYMOUS

45

Pirate Story

Three of us afloat in the meadow by the swing,
    Three of us aboard in the basket on the lea.
Winds are in the air, they are blowing in the spring,
    And waves are on the meadows like the waves there are at sea.

Where shall we adventure, today that we're afloat,
    Wary of the weather and steering by a star?
Shall it be to Africa, a-steering of the boat,
    To Providence, or Babylon, or off to Malabar?

Hi! but here's a squadron a-rowing on to sea –
    Cattle on the meadow a-charging with a roar!
Quick, and we'll escape them, they're as mad as they can be.
    The wicket is the harbour and the garden is the shore.

ROBERT LOUIS STEVENSON

The Captain's Daughter

We were crowded in the cabin –
    Not a soul would dare to sleep –
It was midnight on the waters,
    And a storm was on the deep.

'Tis a fearful thing in winter
    To be shattered by the blast,
And to hear the rattling trumpet
    Thunder: "Cut away the mast!"

So we shuddered there in silence –
    For the stoutest held his breath –
While the hungry sea was roaring
    And the breakers talked with death.

As thus we sat in darkness,
    Each one busy with his prayers,
"We are lost!" the captain shouted,
    As he staggered down the stairs.

But his little daughter whispered,
    As she took his icy hand,
"Isn't God upon the ocean,
    Just the same as on the land?"

Then we kissed the little maiden,
    And we spake in better cheer,
And we anchored safe in harbour
    When the morn was shining clear.

JAMES THOMAS FIELDS

Goodnight

Baby, baby, lay your head
    On your pretty cradle bed;
Shut your eye-peeps now the day
    And the light are gone away;
All the clothes are tucked in tight –
    Little baby dear, goodnight.

Yes, my darling, well I know
    How the bitter wind doth blow;
And the winter's snow and rain
    Patter on the window pane;
But they cannot come in here
    To my little baby dear.

For the window shutteth fast
    Till the stormy night is past,
And the curtains warm are spread
    Round about her cradle bed;
So till morning shineth bright,
    Little baby dear, goodnight.

JANE TAYLOR